EDWARD GOREY: THE OBJECT-LESSON

BLOOMSBURY

For Jason and Barbara Epstein

First published in Great Britain 2002

Copyright © 1958 by Edward Gorey

The moral right of the author has been asserted

Bloomsbury Publishing Plc, 38 Soho Square, London, W1D 3HB

A CIP catalogue record for this book
is available from the British Library

ISBN 0 7475 6083 8

10 9 8 7 6 5 4 3 2

Printed in Singapore by Tien Wah Press

It was already Thursday,

but his lordship's artificial limb could not be found;

therefore, having directed the servants to fill the baths,

he seized the tongs

and set out at once for the edge of the lake,

where the Throbblefoot Spectre still loitered in a distraught manner.

He presented it with a length of string

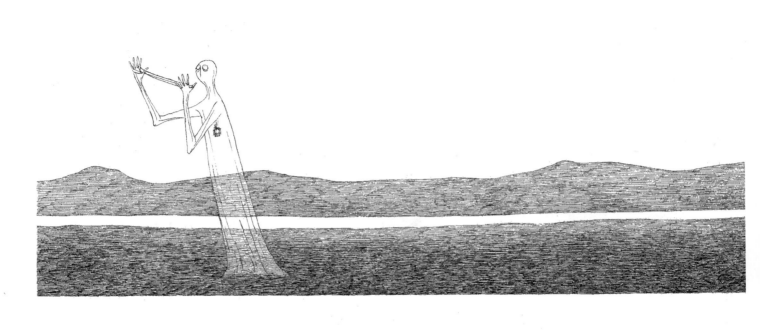

and passed on to the statue of Corrupted Endeavour

to await the arrival of autumn.

Meanwhile, on the tower,

Madame O＿＿＿＿ in conversation with an erstwhile cousin

saw that his moustache was not his own,

on which she flung herself over the parapet

and surreptitiously vanished.

He descended, destroying the letter unread,

and stepped backwards into the water for a better view.

Heavens, how dashing! cried the people in the dinghy,

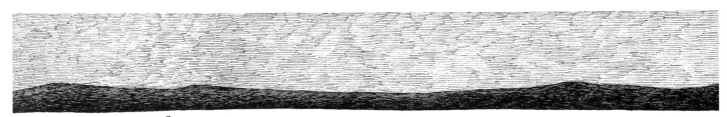

and Echo answered: Count the spoons!

On the shore a bat, or possibly an umbrella,

disengaged itself from the shrubbery,

causing those nearby to recollect the miseries of childhood.

It now became apparent (despite the lack of library paste)

that something had happened to the vicar;

guns began to go off in the distance.

At twilight, however, no message had come from the asylum,

so the others retired to the kiosk,

only to discover the cakes iced a peculiar shade of green

and the tea-urn empty

save for a card on which was written the single word:

Farewell.